FIRST BOOK
OF
BIBLE HEROES

PART ONE

FIRST BOOK
OF
BIBLE HEROES

PART ONE

by DONA Z. MEILACH

illustrations by
EZEKIEL SCHLOSS
assisted by
URI SHULEVITZ

KTAV PUBLISHING HOUSE INC.

Design by EZEKIEL SCHLOSS

TO THE TEACHER AND PARENTS

Through the years, the success of the presentation of Bible Heroes to primary students has been dependent largely upon the teacher's ability to dramatize and tell a story. Often, both the child and teacher felt the stories fell short of exciting a child's imagination and becoming part of his permanent storehouse of knowledge.

The objective of this story book, with the related activity book, is to make the young child a participant rather than simply a passive listener or observer.

Because the reading ability of the primary student is limited, the stories are written to utilize words of the Public School standardized primary grade vocabulary lists.

Beside the actual story of the hero, some connecting material is brought in to give a feeling of historical continuity rather than isolated personalities.

TABLE OF CONTENTS

GOD MAKES A GOOD WORLD

Have you ever looked out of your window and wondered, "How did the trees get here? Where did the flowers come from? How did the world begin?"

The Bible tells us how the world began many, many years ago. There was only darkness and water everywhere, then. God wished there could be a good world.

He thought and planned carefully. He did not want any kind of world. Everything on His world had to be good!

When all His plans were made, God moved over all the waters. On the first day, He said, "Let there be light!"

And there was light. The light became day. The dark became night.

On the second day, as God had planned, He said, "Let there be heaven. Let there be land!"

And there was heaven and land along with the water.

On the third day, He said, "Let the land grow grass. Let there be trees!"

And every kind of seed grew pretty as you please.

On the fourth day, He said, "Now let the heaven have lights. I will make them bright so they will bring day and night. Let these lights tell when summer, winter, spring and fall will come."

And two great lights were in the heaven. They were the sun and the moon.

On the fifth day, God looked at His plan again and said, "Let the earth and water have living creatures!"

Soon, fish filled the water, animals walked on the land. Birds flew about in the sky. When God saw they were good, He blessed them.

On the sixth day, God said, "Now, let there be man!"

He took dust from the ground. He made it into the form of a man. The man became alive. God named him Adam.

God told Adam, "You and the men who come after you will be the rulers over all the living creatures I have made."

God's plan was done. He was pleased with His work and He rested on the seventh day. He blessed this day of rest and made it holy.

Because God rested on the seventh day, everyone takes a day of rest. We call it the Sabbath.

TROUBLE IN THE GARDEN OF EDEN

God planted a great, beautiful garden for Adam to live in. He called it the Garden of Eden.

Adam walked all about to look at the flowers and trees. He picked a pear to eat. It was so good.

He saw one tree that was more beautiful than all the others. It was in the middle of the garden. It had fruit that was bigger and brighter than the fruit on any other tree.

"Stop!" called God. "That fruit you must never touch, even if you want it very much! That is the forbidden tree. If you eat of its fruit, it will bring you nothing but trouble and you will never be happy again."

God gave Adam work to do. Adam took good care of the garden. He gave names to all the living creatures.

But Adam was lonely. So God gave him a wife. Her name was Eve. They were very happy in their Garden of Eden.

A sly and tricky snake lived in the garden, too. One day, Eve was taking care of the grass around the forbidden tree. She heard a hiss-s-s-s, hiss-s-s-s sound. The snake was on the tree!

"Do you know why you must not touch this tree?" asked the snake.

"Because we would have trouble in our life," said Eve.

"Oh, no," said the sneaky snake. "When you eat this bright fruit, you will be as wise as God. You will know what is good and what is evil."

The fruit did look good. And Eve was hungry.

"Eat some!" said the snake. "They are better than all the other fruit!"

So Eve picked some fruit from the forbidden tree. She ran to Adam with them. They both ate the bright red fruit.

Soon Adam and Eve felt funny. Trees that had looked pretty now looked funny. They were afraid. They knew they had done wrong. They tried to hide behind a tree when they heard God.

"You did not mind Me!" called God. "You ate the fruit you were not to touch. Your lives will be changed very much! You cannot live in the Garden of Eden anymore."

God called to the snake and said, "You led Eve to pick the fruit, snake. All your life you shall walk on your belly and eat dust!"

Adam and Eve walked sadly out of the Garden of Eden. They had to work very hard to find food. They never found as much to eat as they had in the Garden of Eden.

Adam and Eve had sons. Two of them were Cain and Abel. Cain and Abel were mean to each other. They were jealous of each other. Adam and Eve were never happy again.

GOD BEGINS AGAIN . . . NOAH'S ARK

Adam and Eve's children grew up and had children. Their children had children. Many years passed and many, many people lived on the earth. God watched the people but He was not pleased. "They are mean and evil," He thought. "They are not kind to each other. They are ruining the good world which I created."

There was only one man who led a good life. His name was Noah.

One day God called, "Noah, Noah! There is going to be a flood. Build an ark of wood. Make it strong, make it good. Hurry! Build it before I flood the earth."

Noah did not waste any time. He and his three sons and their wives worked hard. They cut down trees and made the ark. It looked like a big houseboat.

Then God said, "Noah, take two animals of every kind. Take two of every creature you find into the ark."

Noah and his sons looked everywhere. They took animals and birds, big and small. Then they took food to feed them all.

When everything was ready, God called, "Get everyone into the ark. Close the door. Forty days and nights, it will rain and pour!"

Soon, Noah heard the pitter, patter on the ark. Then he heard thunder. Lightning flashed in the sky. It rained harder and harder. Never had there been such a rain. The flood made the earth turn to mud.

The ark floated on the waters high. But everyone inside was warm and dry. Soon the whole world was covered with water. Not a living thing was left on earth.

Only Noah and those in the ark were alive.

The forty days passed. The rain stopped! A strong wind blew. Noah opened the window of the ark. All he could see was water. Nothing but water.

"Will the water ever dry?" asked one son.

Noah waited a few days. He sent out a dove to look for dry land. The dove came back tired and hungry. There had been no place for him to rest. Noah knew there was no land to be found yet.

Seven days later, he sent the dove out again. This time the bird came back with a green olive leaf.

"Ah," said Noah happily, "soon there will be dry land."

The next morning Noah looked out of the window. "Come here!" he called to his sons. "The ark has come to a stop. It has parked on a mountain top."

His sons looked out of the window. They saw the water going down, down. Soon all the earth would be dry again.

Then, when all the earth was dry, God's voice called to Noah, "Let all the animals out of the ark. Let them go back to the forests and trees."

"Look," said one son. "Look at the beautiful color in the sky." It was the first rainbow!

"That means God will never again flood the earth," Noah told his children. They all thanked God for keeping them safe from the flood.

Noah's children had children. Their children had children. Once again, there were people and animals on God's good earth.

ABRAHAM PASSES THE FIRST TEST

Now you know how God made the earth. You know how He made the first people, Adam and Eve. You know why He sent a flood over the earth. God had a good plan. But when people would not do things God's way, the plan would not work.

God saw that people were doing some strange things. Besides doing things that were not good, people prayed to idols made of wood.

"People need more help," said God. "They are praying to silly kinds of gods. I must find someone on earth to teach them that there is only one God."

One of Noah's great-great-great-grandchildren was a boy named Abraham. All the people in his city believed wooden idols were gods.

"We need corn," they said. "Let us pray to the corn god."

"We need rain," said the people. "Let us pray to the rain god."

When Abraham was a little boy and no one was home, he used the idols to play house. He knew the silly wooden dolls could not do anything. Could they walk? Could they talk? No! Then how could they make a world?

Abraham said to his father, "People do not pray the way they should. How can dolls of wood do any good? There is only one God in the heaven."

Abraham's father said, "Keep your thoughts of God to yourself, Abraham, or you will be put into jail!"

As Abraham grew up, God watched him. God saw how good he was. He thought, "Perhaps Abraham can be the father of people who will do what is right and good. Perhaps it would be best if I gave him a test."

When Abraham was a man God spoke to him. "Take your family. Take everything you need. Leave your town of Haran and start for a new land."

Abraham took his wife, Sarah. He took his sheep and shepherds. He took his gold and riches and moved to the Land of Canaan.

He took his nephew, Lot, with him. Lot took many sheep and shepherds. They found a good place to stay in Canaan. But there was not enough grass for Abraham's sheep and Lot's sheep to eat. Abraham's shepherds began to fight with Lot's shepherds.

"There is much more land in Canaan," Abraham said to Lot. "You pick the land you want and I will take what is left."

Lot picked the best land with the thickest grass and plenty of water.

Abraham took what was left. God was pleased that Abraham was not selfish.

Abraham and Sarah were very happy. They built an altar to God. Every morning and night, Abraham thanked God for their good home.

One evening as Abraham prayed, he said, "I wonder who my people will be. I am getting very old. But Sarah and I have no children."

God heard Abraham and said, "Look up at the stars and count them if you can, Abraham. You will be the father of more people than there are stars in the sky. You must believe in Me and do as I ask. When you have a son, you must teach him to do the same."

Abraham knew God would ask him to do only what was right.

THE FINAL TEST

Years passed. Yet Sarah and Abraham had no children.

God put Abraham to many tests and he passed them all. But the final test was still to come!

As Abraham sat in the doorway of his tent one hot afternoon, he looked up and saw three men.

"You must be hot and tired," Abraham said. "Sit under the tree and rest. I will bring you food and water."

The men rested. They ate fruit and meat. When they were ready to go, one man spoke, "Thank you. You are a good man. May all your wishes come true."

Abraham said, "I am a happy man. I have a good wife. I have many sheep and goats. I only wish we had a son. But now my wife and I are too old."

The men smiled. "Good-bye," they said. "May your son grow strong and healthy!"

What did they mean? Who were they? Where did they come from? Abraham and Sarah asked each other.

Soon after, Sarah had a baby boy. "Those men were angels of the Lord," thought Abraham as he looked at his new son.

They named the baby, Isaac, because it means "he will laugh." And Isaac brought love and fun to Sarah and Abraham.

Then one day, when Isaac was about your age, God put Abraham to the final test.

"Abraham," the voice of God called. "Take your son, Isaac, to the top of a hill. Place him on a burning altar so he will be your gift to Me."

Abraham's heart nearly broke. "God must have a reason for asking me to do this," he thought. The next day, Abraham said to Isaac, "Come, my boy. It is time for us to give God a beautiful gift."

When they got to the top of the hill, Isaac helped his father gather wood for the altar.

When the fire was burning high, Isaac was very pleased with the job. He turned to his father and asked, "Where is the ram, father? Don't we always give a ram to the Lord on the altar?"

Abraham took Isaac in his arms. He said sadly. "This time my son, you are our gift to the Lord."

Just then, God called from the sky. "Stop! Don't take another step, Abraham! Put the boy down! You have proved your trust in Me is great!"

Abraham heard another voice. It was a ram. It was caught in a bush. Isaac ran and caught the ram. They put the ram on the altar as their gift to God.

As they prayed, God blessed them. He said "Abraham I will make you the father of a great nation. They shall be called Hebrews."

ISAAC GETS A WIFE

Isaac grew up to be a fine, handsome young man. He helped his father care for the sheep. He was kind to the shepherds. He made friends with their neighbors in Canaan.

Sarah died and Abraham grew very old. "It is time Isaac had a wife," Abraham said to his servant, Eliezer. "Go to our old city of Haran. Find Isaac a good wife."

"What if I find a girl who does not want to come to Canaan? May Isaac live in Haran?" asked Eliezer.

"No! Never!" said Abraham. "Isaac must stay in Canaan. God has given us this land. We must stay and make it a good land!"

The next morning, Eliezer put food and gifts on ten camels. He started for the far off city of Haran.

Picking a wife for another man is not an easy job. Eliezer wondered how he would know which girl would be right for Isaac. By the time he got to Haran, he had a plan.

In those days, everyone had to get water from a well. As the women and girls came to fill their water jugs, Eliezer asked one, and then another, if he could have a drink. No one was kind to the stranger.

It was getting dark. Eliezer was giving up hope. Then a beautiful young girl came through the gate. Eliezer watched her fill her jug. He ran to her and said, "Please, let me drink a little water, I am so thirsty."

"Drink, sir," she said sweetly. She tipped the heavy jug so the old man could drink.

"Your camels look hot, sir," said the girl. "Let me bring water for them also."

She worked fast. Soon all the camels were watered. "Could she be the girl for Isaac?" Eliezer wondered. "I must make sure."

"What is your name and the name of your family?" said Eliezer.

"My name is Rebekah," answered the girl. When she told Eliezer who her family was, he nearly jumped with joy. Rebekah came from the same family that Abraham came from.

Eliezer asked, "Do you know of a place I may sleep tonight?"

"I am sure you will be welcome at my father's house," said Rebekah. She ran home to tell her parents that a guest was coming.

That evening, Eliezer ate dinner with Rebekah's family. He told them he had come to Haran to find a wife for Isaac. "I think I have found her," he said. "I would like to take Rebekah to Canaan to be Isaac's wife."

The family was pleased. "Only God could have planned this meeting so well," said Rebekah's brother. "But you must ask Rebekah."

Rebekah smiled. "Yes, I will be happy to go with Eliezer."

Isaac and Rebekah fell in love as soon as they met. She became his wife and they were very, very happy.

JACOB AND ESAU

Isaac and Rebekah were so happy when they had twin sons. They named one son Jacob and the other Esau. They loved their boys very much.

Jacob was quiet, gentle and smart. He took care of his father's sheep and land. Often, he helped his mother with her work.

Esau loved to hunt more than anything else in the world. With his bow and arrow and knife of sharp stone, he would hunt in the woods all alone. He was tall and strong and often, he said, "No animals scare me."

Jacob and Esau loved each other. But, sometimes they would fight. One day, when Esau came home from hunting, he was very tired and hungry.

Jacob was cooking a pot of thick soup. It smelled good.

Esau almost fell on the ground, "Please, Jacob, hurry. Give me some food to eat. I am so weak I cannot stand on my feet. I will let you have the blessings of the first born if you will give me some of the food you are cooking. What good will blessings and riches be to me if I die of hunger?"

Jacob watched Esau gobble his food. He thought, "Esau is very foolish to give me everything for a dish of soup. I am afraid he will be sorry he made such a promise."

A short time later, Esau married a girl from Canaan. The girl prayed to wooden idols. Isaac and Rebekah were not happy. They wanted their boys to marry girls from Haran where Rebekah was born.

"We must send Jacob to Haran to find a wife," said Rebekah.

Isaac called Jacob. He said, "My son, you must visit your Uncle Laban. Stay with him until you find a girl you love. Marry her and bring her back to Canaan."

"It is a long trip through the desert," said Rebekah. "I will give you food and water. Be careful."

Isaac gave Jacob his best blessing. Esau saw his father blessing Jacob.

"It is not fair," Esau said to himself. "I foolishly gave away my right to blessings of the first born. I also married an idol worshipper and made my parents angry with me."

"Soon my father will die," thought Esau. "Then I will get even with my brother, Jacob!"

JACOB DREAMS OF A LADDER

Jacob put clothes, food, water and gifts on his camel. He waved good-bye to his father and mother and started off.

His camel's strong legs carried him a long way through the hot, sandy desert. When night came, Jacob stopped to rest and eat. There was a stone near by and Jacob used it as a pillow.

In a few minutes, he was asleep and dreaming.

He dreamed he saw a giant ladder on the ground next to him. He looked for the top of it. He looked higher and higher until he almost fell back. He could not see the top of the ladder! It went up-up-up through the stars and into the sky.

"What kind of a ladder could this be?" wondered Jacob. He lay very still. His heart beat fast. He saw angels running up and down the steps of the ladder.

Then, slowly, softly, he heard a voice call, "Jacob, Jacob, I am the Lord. I am the God of your grandfather, Abraham, and your father, Isaac. I am your God, too. I will take care of you."

Jacob listened but the voice stopped. The ladder was gone. It was as if the Lord had pulled it to heaven with Him.

Jacob sat up. He was awake now.

"Maybe it was only a dream," said Jacob. "But I am sure the Lord was here and He spoke to me."

Jacob took the stone he used as a pillow and set it up as an altar to the Lord. "This is truly a holy place," said Jacob. "I will give this place a name."

Jacob named it "Bethel" which means "House of God."

JACOB MEETS RACHEL AT THE WELL

The next day, Jacob reached the city of Haran where his Uncle Laban lived. He stopped at a well where shepherds were watering their sheep. "Can you tell me where the house of Laban is?" asked Jacob.

"Of course," said one man. "But here comes his daughter, Rachel. She can take you to him."

Jacob looked at the lovely young girl leading her sheep to the well. He helped her water the animals. When the sheep were watered, the girl said, "Thank you."

But Jacob did not say, "You are welcome." Jacob bent over and kissed her.

You can guess how surprised she was!

Jacob laughed. He twirled her around and said, "That is the right way to greet a cousin."

"Rachel," he said, "Your father, Laban, is my uncle."

Rachel was very happy. She took Jacob home to meet her father and her sister.

"You must stay and work for me," said his Uncle Laban. "I will pay you for your work."

"I do not want pay," said Jacob. "I would like Rachel to be my wife, if she is willing."

This time, Rachel kissed Jacob and said, "Yes, I will marry you, Jacob."

"The watering place brings my family good luck," said Jacob. "My mother, Rebekah, was first seen at the well and became my father's wife. When I saw you at the well, Rachel, I knew you were the girl I would ask to be my wife."

Jacob and Rachel lived with Laban for many years. Jacob worked hard. He became rich and had many children.

CAN JACOB GO BACK TO CANAAN?

One evening when Jacob and Rachel were sitting quietly, Jacob said, "My father, Isaac, is very old now. I would like to see him again. I would like to go back to Canaan to live."

"But what about your brother, Esau?" asked Rachel. "Aren't you afraid he will cause trouble for you?"

"I will find that out when I return," said Jacob. "Perhaps Esau forgot how angry he was. It was so many years ago. But I must go home to the land of my father."

Jacob and Rachel packed their camels. They put their children on camels too. They said good-bye to Laban and began their trip to Canaan.

Jacob sent two men ahead to find Esau. "Give my brother these sheep and camels, goats and horses as gifts from me," he said. "Tell Esau I am coming home."

When the two men came back, they said, "We found your brother, Esau. We gave him your message. He is coming to meet you with four hundred men."

"Four hundred men!" cried Jacob. He was worried. "Would Esau try to harm my family?"

That night, Jacob did not sleep well. He dreamed he was fighting with someone. He did not know who it was. In his dream, Jacob threw the man to the ground. Then the man said, "You have won. You have done many things to put yourself in God's favor. Do not be afraid. From now on, your name is ISRAEL, which means Prince of God."

In the morning, Jacob heard horses and men coming his way. Bravely, he went to meet Esau and his men. Esau got down from his horse. The two brothers looked at each other. Then Esau put out his hand and said, "Welcome home, Jacob." They hugged one another and laughed and cried. They were happy to be together again.

Jacob remembered his dream. Now he knew what it meant. It was God's way of telling him that he was living the way God wanted him to live. He had learned to do good and be wise. He has earned the name ISRAEL. He was a "Prince of God."

From that day on, Jacob was called Israel and all his children were the Children of Israel. That is how the Land of Canaan got its new name, the Land of Israel.

JOSEPH HAS TROUBLE WITH HIS BROTHERS

Now everyone called Jacob by his new name, Israel. Israel and his twelve sons made their home in Canaan. Like all fathers, Israel loved his sons. He was proud of them.

There was one son, who was younger than the others. His name was Joseph. While the older brothers took care of the sheep, Israel kept Joseph home to keep him company.

Israel made a special coat for Joseph. And that coat caused trouble for Joseph.

The coat was not like any coat you have ever seen. It was made of many beautiful colors . . . reds, blues, purples, greens.

When Joseph's brothers saw the coat of many colors, they were jealous.

"Why couldn't father make a coat of many colors for me, too?" asked one brother.

"You are not his pet," answered another. "Only Joseph is father's pet."

Joseph saw that his brothers were angry. But his father said, "Don't worry about them, Joseph. You wear the coat. It looks fine on you."

Now Joseph loved to dream. Often, he told his family about his dreams. Sometimes they made fun of him.

One day Joseph said, "Last night I had a dream about my family. We were all making bundles of wheat. My bundle stood up straight. Your bundles came around and bowed down to my bundle."

They all laughed. "What a silly boy!" But one brother got mad. "Do you think that means you will be king over us? You?"

"I don't really know what it means," said Joseph. "But I had another dream, too. I dreamed the sun and moon and eleven stars bowed down to me."

His brothers became very angry. "You do think you are better than we are, don't you? Well, we shall see!"

Joseph was surprised. He didn't want to make them angry. He thought, "I will not tell them any more of my dreams."

A few days later, Israel sent Joseph to take food to his brothers. When they saw him coming in his bright coat, one brother said, "Here comes the dreamer! Let us stop his silly talk about dreams. Let us kill him!"

Another brother said, "Oh no, we must not kill him. Let us have some fun with him. Put him in that big, deep hole in the ground."

"Hello," called Joseph. The brothers grabbed him. They tore off his coat of many colors. They tied him up and threw him into the hole.

The brothers ate the food Joseph brought. Joseph cried and screamed, "Take me out!" But the brothers only ate and ate and ate.

Then one brother saw a caravan. Camels and men were taking riches and food to Egypt. "What good is it if we hurt Joseph? He is our brother. Let us sell him to those men."

"Good idea," said all the brothers. "And we will have some money for ourselves."

They pulled Joseph from the hole. They took him to the caravan.

The men looked Joseph over carefully. "We can use a strong boy. Here is our money." The men put Joseph on a camel and took him away.

The brothers tore Joseph's coat. They dipped it into the blood from a sheep. When they came home, they acted very sad. "Look, father," they said, "we found the beautiful coat you made for Joseph, but we did not find Joseph."

"He must have been eaten by a wild animal!" cried Israel. And while their father cried, the boys winked at one another.

JOSEPH GOES TO JAIL

The men took Joseph to Egypt, many miles away from his home in Canaan. They sold the food and cotton and spices they had on their camels. They also sold Joseph.

They sold Joseph to a rich man who had a big house in Egypt. Joseph was his slave. He had to do whatever the rich man asked.

Joseph was honest. He worked very hard for his master. The rich man was very pleased with his new slave. He made Joseph the manager of all his property. One day the rich man's wife asked Joseph to do something wrong. Joseph refused.

That made the woman angry. She ran to her husband and told him a lie. She told him that Joseph had been rude to her.

The rich man believed his wife's lies. He had Joseph put in jail.

The jail was dark and dirty. Joseph's cell had one small window. Every night he would look at the sky and pray to God. The keeper of the jail liked Joseph. He saw that he was kind. He said, "You will be my helper."

One day, Pharaoh, King of Egypt, found a fly in the bread he was eating. He was angry with his servants. He sent two men to jail.

"They are the Pharaoh's butler and baker," said the keeper. "Take good care of them, Joseph."

Every morning, Joseph brought them their breakfast.

"Why do you look so sad, butler and baker?" asked Joseph one morning.

The butler said, "I had a dream last night. I do not know what it means."

The baker said, "I had a dream last night, too. If only someone could tell me what it means."

"Is that what is making you so mad?" laughed Joseph. "What did you dream? I will tell you what your dream means."

"Let me tell my dream first," said the butler. "I saw a small tree. It had three branches. The branches had buds that opened up to be juicy ripe grapes. I picked the grapes and put their juice into Pharaoh's cup. He drank it all up."

"That's easy," said Joseph. "The branches mean that in three days Pharaoh will call you to work for him again. The cup means you are to serve him as you have done before."

The butler was happy to hear his dream had such a fine meaning. "You are a wise man, Joseph. How can I thank you?"

"You can do me a great favor," Joseph said. "When you go back to the palace, please ask your king to take me out of jail. I was taken from the Land of the Hebrews. I have done nothing wrong."

Then the baker said, "Now tell me quickly what my dream means. I had three baskets of bread on my head. I was taking them to the king. Some birds saw the bread and ate it all up. There were only a few crumbs left for the king."

"Is that all there is to your dream?" asked Joseph.

"That is all," said the baker. "Does it mean the king will take me back too?"

"Oh no," said Joseph sadly. "The king is still mad at you. He does not want you back at all."

Joseph was right. The butler was called back to work for the king. The baker was not called back.

THE KING'S DREAM

Do you think the butler remembered that Joseph asked a favor of him?

He did not.

Joseph stayed in jail for two more years. He wondered if he would ever be free again.

Then one day, the keeper ran to him and said, "Joseph, come quickly. Change your clothes. Pharaoh, the King, has sent for you!"

Soon, Joseph was standing before the great Pharaoh in the beautiful room of the palace.

Pharaoh looked at the young man and seemed pleased with him.

Pharaoh said, "I have had a strange dream. Not one of my wise men can tell me what it means. My butler said you can tell what dreams mean. Is that true?"

"I cannot do it alone," said Joseph. "God will help me tell you the meaning of your dream."

"Well," said Pharaoh. "Let me tell you my dream. See what you can make of it."

This is what Pharaoh dreamed: Seven fat cows were eating grass. Along came seven thin cows and they ate and they ate and they ate until there was no more grass. The thin cows were still hungry so they looked for more to eat. They saw the fat cows and ate them all up. No matter how much they ate, they were still thin and hungry.

Then, the same thing happened with seven ears of corn. Seven fat ears of corn were eaten by seven thin ears of corn.

Joseph said, "Oh King, I think God has told me what your dreams mean. The seven fat cows and fat corn mean this: For seven years corn will grow in Egypt. The people will have plenty to eat.

"The seven thin cows and thin corn mean this: For the next seven years there will be no food. All your people will go hungry. Many may die."

"What can I do? Where can I find a wise man who can make the corn grow?" asked the Pharaoh.

"Only God can make corn grow," said Joseph. "You must grow more corn than you need in the good years. You can store it and have it for the bad years. Then your people will have food to eat when the corn does not grow. They will not go hungry and die."

"Your plan is very wise," said Pharaoh. "You are wiser than all my wise men! Joseph, you must take care of storing the corn. You can take all the men and gold you need. You shall rule over all the land. Only I, Pharaoh, shall be above you."

And Joseph became the second most important man in Egypt!

CAN JOSEPH FEED THE WORLD?

Joseph had storehouses built in every city to hold the corn. He went to every farmer in Egypt. He told them, "Pharaoh says you must grow more corn than you need. Bring the corn you do not eat to the big storehouses."

The people brought their corn to Joseph's storehouses. For seven years, Joseph put corn in the storehouses until they were filled to the top.

When the seven years were over, corn would not grow in most parts of the world. Only the people of Egypt had food to eat because Joseph had saved the corn. Soon, people from other lands came to Egypt to buy corn.

Even in the land of Canaan, there was no corn. Joseph's father and brothers were very hungry.

His father said to his sons, "I have heard you can buy corn in Egypt. All of you go and bring back corn so we will not die. I will keep Benjamin, my youngest son, to take care of me while you are gone."

The ten brothers went to Egypt with money and gifts to buy corn. They went to the storehouse. Whom do you think they saw?

It was Joseph. They did not know him. It had been many years since they had sold their brother. Now he was a grown man dressed in fine clothes.

But Joseph knew them. At first, he did not know what to do. Then he said to himself, "I will give them what they want, but I will test them. I will see if they have changed."

When the brothers stood before him, Joseph asked, "What do you want? Where are you from?"

"We came from Canaan to buy food," they said.

"That is not true!" shouted Joseph. "I think you are spies. You came to see how you could steal corn!"

"Oh no Sir!" said the brothers. "We are telling the truth! At home we have an old father and our young brother Benjamin, who are very hungry.

"If you are not lying, bring your brother here. Then I will give you corn," said Joseph.

"But Sir," said the oldest brother. "I beg you. Our father needs Benjamin to care for him. We do not have enough food to make the trip again."

"Well . . ." said Joseph. "I will give you a little corn this time. Next time, if you do not bring your brother, you will go to jail as spies."

The next time the brothers needed corn, they took Benjamin to Egypt with them. When Joseph saw his brother, Benjamin, he could no longer act mean.

"Do you know who I am?" he asked his brothers.

They shook their heads and said, "No."

"I am Joseph, your brother whom you sold as a slave."

They could not believe it. At first they were afraid of their brother Joseph.

But Joseph said, "Do not be afraid. It was not your fault. God sent me to Egypt. It was He who sent me here so the people of the world would not go hungry."

Then Joseph said, "Hurry, bring my father to Egypt. I have missed him all these years. In Egypt there is enough food for all of you and your families."

Israel was happy to learn Joseph was alive. He and his sons took their families and everything they owned. They moved to Egypt.

Pharaoh learned Joseph's family was coming to Egypt. He gave them the best farm land in the country. He gave them the land called Goshen.

And that is how the Children of Israel moved out of Canaan and came to live in the land of Egypt.

THE HEBREWS BECOME SLAVES

Joseph's brothers were happy in Goshen. The children of Israel had children. Their children had children. Soon, there were many Hebrew families.

The people tried to live as they lived in Canaan. They spoke Hebrew. They had Hebrew names. They prayed to one God.

Many years passed and a new Pharaoh ruled over Egypt. He was not kind like the other Pharaoh. He was mean and selfish. He wanted everyone to do what he said.

For many years the new Pharaoh watched the Hebrew people. He became very angry.

"Why must the Hebrews be different from the Egyptians?" he shouted. "Why don't they wear the same clothes the Egyptians wear? Why must they speak Hebrew? Do they think their God is better than I am? Don't they know that I am god because I am king of Egypt?"

Pharaoh called his wise men, "There are too many Hebrews!" he shouted. "If there is a war they may fight against us. Then Egypt would belong to the Hebrews!"

The wise men were afraid of Pharaoh, so one man said, "Oh, Great Pharaoh. You are right. Something must be done to the Hebrews."

Another wise man said, "Yes, yes, O King. What can we do to the Hebrews?"

"Make the Hebrews our slaves!" shouted Pharaoh.

He laughed a cruel, wicked laugh. "I want a beautiful temple and a palace to live in. The Hebrews must do the hard work. I will show them who is King in Egypt."

The wicked Pharaoh made the Hebrew people leave their farms. He made them carry big, heavy stones. Egyptian men became bosses over the Hebrews. They used whips to make the Hebrews build the Pharaoh's temples.

Even the children were put to work. They had to make bricks. They had to bring food and water to the old people who were working in the hot sun.

Pharaoh hoped the hard work would make many Hebrews die. Instead, it seemed the Hebrews grew stronger and had bigger and bigger families.

"There are still too many Hebrews!" said the Pharaoh. "If they do not die from slavery, I must think of something else."

Then Pharaoh gave a new order: "From now on, every Hebrew boy that is born must be killed. Only the girls shall live and be my slaves."

A BABY BOY IS SAVED

Soon after Pharaoh had given his terrible order, a baby boy was born to a woman named Jochebed. For three months she hid her baby when Pharaoh's men came to search the Hebrew homes. She knew she could not hide him much longer.

"Come," she said to her older children, Miriam and Aaron. "We will put the baby in a basket and float him down the Nile River. Maybe a kind Egyptian woman will find him."

Aaron helped make a basket that would not sink.

Miriam and her mother tucked the baby into the basket. Miriam pushed the basket into the Nile River and followed it as it floated down the river. It caught in the reeds near the shore. Egyptian women were sunning and swimming.

Pharaoh's daughter was dipping her toes in the water.

"There is a basket in the water," the princess said to her maid. "Bring it to me. Let us see what is in it."

She looked inside. "A baby!" she cried. "Oh, it must be hungry. Look how it chews its fingers."

The princess knew he must be a Hebrew baby. She felt sorry for him.

Miriam was watching from nearby. She called softly to the princess. "I know a Hebrew woman who will nurse him for you."

"Please, bring her to me at once," said the princess. "I will pay her well."

Miriam ran to her mother. "The princess has found the baby. She is going to let him live. She wants you to take care of him, mother!"

The princess said to Jochebed, "Nurse this boy. I am willing to pay. But bring him to me every day. I will raise him as my own son. I will call him 'Moses,' because that means, 'I drew him out of the water!'"

Jochebed took care of Moses until he was three years old. She taught him he was a Hebrew and Moses never forgot.

When Moses lived at the palace, the princess taught him how to be an Egyptian. Often Pharaoh played with Moses and told him stories. He grew up to be a handsome prince. Everyone liked Moses.

But the princess worried, "What would happen to Moses if Pharaoh learned he was really a Hebrew and not an Egyptian son?"

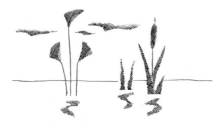

MOSES ESCAPES FROM EGYPT

One day it happened!

Moses saw an Egyptian boss beating an old Hebrew slave with his whip.

"Stop!" cried Moses. "That poor old man is too weak to work any more."

The Egyptian kept on beating the old man. Moses got mad. He hit the Egyptian so hard, the man fell down. Moses tried to move him, but he was dead.

The old Hebrew slave helped Moses bury the Egyptian. He was afraid. He said to Moses, "When Pharaoh learns you have killed an Egyptian to save a slave, he will kill you."

"You are right, old man," said Moses. "I shall run away and hide." He ran to Jochebed's house to say good-bye.

"Hurry and leave Egypt, Moses," she said. "I have heard that Pharaoh's soldiers are looking for you now. Go, my son, God will be with you."

Moses got out of Egypt in time. He went to the Land of Midian.

He came to a watering place and rested.

Seven girls were watering their father's sheep. Moses helped them. The girls thanked Moses and said, "Come home with us, stranger. We would like you to meet our father and have dinner with us."

The father listened to Moses' story. "You are welcome to live here with us," he said. "I need a strong, young man to help me and my daughters take care of the sheep."

Moses stayed. He married Zipporah, the oldest daughter. They had two fine sons.

Moses lived a good life in Midian. Yet, he was not happy.

Moses knew the Hebrews were still slaves in Egypt. As he watched his sheep. he often thought he could hear the sound of the whips slap across the backs of his people.

Moses thought, "If only I could do something so the Hebrews would not be slaves."

THE BUSH THAT WOULD NOT BURN

One sunny day, Moses was watching the sheep. They were eating grass on the side of the hill.

A little lamb ran away from its mother. Moses ran after it and caught it. He saw something bright red not far away. He walked closer to it. It was a bush on fire!

"That is strange," he thought. "The bush is on fire, but it does not burn up."

He walked closer to the bush. The fire got bigger and hotter. But still the branches were not burning. The leaves were fresh and green.

"Moses! Moses!" a voice called. It seemed to be coming from inside the great fire.

"Who is calling me?" Moses looked all around but there was no one. He knew the lamb could not call his name.

"Moses," the voice called again. "Take off your shoes. You are standing on holy ground. I am the God of Abraham, Isaac and Jacob."

Moses was afraid. "Why is God talking to me?"

"Moses!" said God. "My people must be taken out of Egypt! Go. Lead them to the Land of Canaan where there is milk and honey!"

"How can I do it?" asked Moses. "Pharaoh will have me killed as soon as I put a foot into Egypt. I am afraid!"

"I will send your brother, Aaron, with you," said God. Moses was still afraid.

"Throw your shepherd's rod on the ground!" said God. Moses threw down the rod. It turned into a snake!

"Now pick up the snake by the tail!" said God. Moses picked up the snake. It became his rod again!

He looked at the bush. Its branches were covered with green leaves waving in the soft breeze. The fire was gone!

Moses was sure now. He knew God was with him.

Moses quickly led the sheep home. "Come, Zipporah," he said to his wife. "Get the children ready. Let us load the donkeys. We are going back to Egypt!"

PHARAOH LAUGHS AT MOSES

Moses met Aaron. They went to Egypt together. They were not happy when they saw how the Hebrews were treated. The slaves were tired, dirty and thin. The new Pharaoh was mean. The slaves worked hard but were not given enough to eat.

Moses stood among his people and said, "God has sent me to put an end to your slavery and lead you out of Egypt!"

The Hebrews listened to Moses. But they warned, "Pharaoh will not listen to you. He says he is god. He is afraid of no one."

Moses and Aaron bravely went to the great palace. They walked on a red rug through the large room that led to the king's throne.

There were officers of the court all around Pharaoh. He was dressed in red and blue and gold silks. On his head sat a gold crown heavy with jewels.

Moses and Aaron walked to the steps of the throne. They did not bow. Moses said, "The God of Israel has sent us to lead the Hebrews out of Egypt. Let my people go, Pharaoh!"

Pharaoh's eyes turned mean. He was so angry his face turned as red as the rug.

"I am the only god!" he boomed. "You say there is another God? Show me what He can do that I cannot."

Moses threw his rod on the floor. It turned into a long, hissing snake.

Pharaoh laughed a loud, mean laugh.

"Wise men!" he called. "Show this fool how good his trick is!"

The wise men threw their rods on the floor. All the rods turned into snakes. Before Pharaoh could laugh again, Moses' snake quickly turned and ate up all the others.

"Get out of here!" cried Pharaoh. "From now on, your people will work harder than ever! Not only must they make the bricks to build my temples, they must find the straw to make the bricks. If they do not make all the bricks they should, my men will beat them with clubs of wood."

The two brothers went from the palace. When the Hebrews heard what happened, they were angry with Moses. "What have you done to us with your tricks? Now Pharaoh will kill us!"

Moses prayed. "What have I done, Oh Lord? When I spoke to Pharaoh, I was not clever. He will treat the Hebrews worse than ever!"

God said, "Do not fear, Moses. I will free the Hebrews. You shall see what I will do to Pharaoh. He will be sorry he ever saw a Hebrew!"

GOD PUNISHES PHARAOH

Again and again, Moses went to Pharaoh and said, "Let my people go! If you do not, God will punish you."

Pharaoh did not listen to Moses. Then terrible things began to happen in Egypt. First, the Nile River turned to blood. For one week, the people had no water to drink.

Next, God sent frogs into Egypt. People had frogs in their houses, in their beds, in their food.

Then God sent lice. Everyone scratched and scratched. Then he sent wild beasts. Pharaoh was afraid.

"Tell your God to stop!" Pharaoh cried in anger. "I will let your people go, Moses!"

But when the animals were gone, Pharaoh smiled his cruel smile. He broke his promise. He would not let the Hebrew people go.

Nine times God punished the Egyptians. Nine times Pharaoh said to Moses, "Tell your God to stop. I will let your people go." And nine times he broke his promise.

The tenth time, the Lord was very angry. He called to Moses and said, "Tomorrow night, the first child of every family in Egypt will die. Only the Hebrew children will be passed over."

Pharaoh's son died and so did the first child in every Egyptian family.

"Enough! Enough!" cried Pharaoh. "Take your people and go! Pray to your God! Go from the land of Egypt forever. You are free! Only stop this terrible thing that is happening to us."

Moses and Aaron ran to the Hebrews. "Hurry, hurry," they called. "Take what you need. We must hurry out of Egypt now!"

The men packed as fast as they could. Everybody carried something. Even the children had little bundles.

The women took the food. They packed so fast the women had no time to bake.

Moses led the Hebrews to the shore of the Red Sea. As they reached the sea they heard the noises of horses' feet. Hundreds of soldiers and chariots were chasing them. Pharaoh had changed his cruel mind again.

How were they to escape? How could they get across the deep sea? Suddenly the Red Sea split and a path of dry land opened up. The Hebrews hurried across just in time! Pharaoh's soldiers followed the Hebrews into the sea. They came closer and closer. They shot arrows at the Hebrews.

When the last Hebrew had crossed, the waters of the Red Sea came together again. All the Egyptian soldiers drowned.

The Hebrews were free at last. Moses' sister, Miriam, led them in songs and dances. They thanked God for His help.

TO MOUNT SINAI

The Hebrews looked around. They saw a wilderness. There were no cities, no farms, nothing. They were afraid. They did not know how to act as free people. For hundreds of years they had had masters to tell them what to do. Now they could not think for themselves.

Some cried, "Let us go back to Egypt. We will starve

here." But when their food was gone, God dropped food from heaven so they would not go hungry. It was called "manna" from heaven.

"See, God is always with you," said Moses. "Trust Him. He will look after you."

They said, "Yes, yes, Moses." But when something went wrong, they cried to go back to Egypt.

Moses listened to his people. Some were not kind. Others told lies. Some were fighting. "I love these people," Moses said to his friend Joshua, "but they are not ready to go to the Land of Canaan." Moses wondered how he could teach his people to live together in peace.

Three months after they left Egypt, they came to a green valley at the bottom of Mount Sinai.

"Let us stop here and rest," said Moses.

That night, Moses sat under the stars, deep in thought. Softly, as in a dream, he heard God's voice. "Call your people together, Moses. I want to speak to them so they may hear My Great Laws. Only if they follow these Laws and trust in Me, will they live together in peace. Only My Laws will make them a great group of people!"

In the morning, Moses called all the Hebrews together.

They looked up at the big mountain. Suddenly, there was a loud noise. Smoke rolled down the mountain side. God's voice was heard by all.

"I will give you TEN COMMANDMENTS," said God's voice. "You must promise to obey them!"

The Hebrews promised to obey God's Commandments.

These are some of the Commandments God gave the Hebrews that morning from Mount Sinai.

I am the Lord, your God . . . you shall have no other God.

Remember the Sabbath, to keep it holy.

Honor your father and your mother.

Do not steal.

Do not tell lies.

Do not be jealous of things your friends have.

Then the Lord's voice called to the Hebrews again. "Send Moses to Me. Send him to the very top of the mountain!"

The voice of God was heard no more. The people spoke softly to one another. "Yes, yes," they said. "God has spoken to us. He is watching over us." And they were not afraid.

THE GOLDEN CALF

Moses told his brother Aaron to take care of the people and their needs. Moses took Joshua with him. They started up the mountain.

Moses was gone for many days. The people began to wonder, "What has happened to Moses? Maybe he is not coming back!"

Someone said, "How do we know God has not taken Moses from us?"

Another said, "We all heard God, but did we see Him? No! The Egyptians had gods they could see. We need a god we can see!"

"The Egyptian gods can't do anything," said Aaron. "Give me your earrings and rings. You will see how silly it is to have a god like the Egyptians have."

The women took off their earrings and rings. They threw them into a fire. They all melted. Aaron made the earrings and rings into a golden calf. He laughed when he showed the calf to the people.

But the people did not laugh. They began to sing and dance. They bowed low to the metal animal. They sang prayers of joy.

Aaron and his sister Miriam tried to stop them. The singing and praying grew louder and louder. The people built an altar in front of the calf and had a big dinner.

The Lord heard all the noise. He looked down. "Go back to your people, Moses," He said. "See how they have kept the Commandments I gave them!"

Moses carried tablets made of stone. The Ten Commandments were written on them.

On their way down the mountain, Joshua said, "There is noise coming from the camp. It sounds like our people are at war!"

Moses listened. "It is the sound of people singing."

When Moses came to the camp, he saw the golden calf. He saw the people dancing. He saw the people praying to the golden calf.

"What have you done?" he shouted in anger. "You have made an idol! You are praying to it! Have you forgotten your promise to God?"

Moses threw down the stone tablets with the Ten Commandments written on them. They broke into hundreds of pieces. He pushed over the golden calf. He threw it onto the fire and it melted into powder.

The Hebrews stood silent and afraid. They knew they had done wrong. They told Moses they were sorry.

That night, Moses called to God and asked Him to forgive his people.

God was angry. "What is the matter with the Hebrews?" He said. "They cannot remember on one day, a promise they made the day before. They must be punished!"

Moses begged, "Oh Lord, after all You have done to free the Hebrews from Egypt, would You hurt them now? Then the Egyptians would laugh. They would say the Hebrews' God led them out of Egypt only to hurt them. If that is the God they wish to trust, let them!"

And God answered, "I will erase the sin from My book. If they sin once more, I must punish them."

Again Moses went to the top of Mount Sinai. He stayed for forty days and forty nights.

When Moses came down his face glowed. In his hands were the two stone tablets. The Children of Israel danced around him. He gave them the Ten Commandments. They promised they would always obey the Commandments.

THE SPIES REPORT

The Hebrews built a tent and a beautiful ark to keep the Ten Commandments safe. The ark looked like a beautiful big box. It had four poles so it could be carried from one place to another. The people were proud of the ark and their Laws. Every Sabbath, they opened the ark and remembered how God had helped them.

For more than a year, the Hebrews walked through the wilderness toward the Land of Canaan. They took the Laws with them everywhere.

One morning, Moses called his people together. He pointed to the mountains and said, "On the other side of those mountains is the land God promised the Children of Abraham, Isaac and Jacob. It is the Promised Land for all Children of Israel."

"Is it really a land of milk and honey?" the people asked.

"We will send spies to learn about the land," said Moses.

Joshua said, "I will go."

Other men said, "I will go." Soon there were twelve strong men.

The spies were gone for forty days. They came back with a big bunch of grapes. It was so big, it took two men to carry it on a pole.

"What did you find in Canaan?" the people asked.

Some of the spies said, "Canaan looks like good farm land. It does look like a land of milk and honey. But the cities have great walls around them. The people look like giants!"

"Like giants?" the Hebrews asked.

"Yes, like great giants!" said the spies. "They look strong and fearless. We will have trouble if we have to fight them."

When the Hebrews heard this terrible news, some cried, "Oh, we should have stayed in Egypt!"

Others ran to Moses and Aaron. They said, "Take us back to Egypt. Our wives and children will be killed if we fight giants."

Joshua tried to calm the Hebrews. "Those people are not giants. We did not get close to them. The Lord is on our side. He has helped us before and He will help us again."

The Hebrews would not listen to Joshua. "We will all be killed by giants," they shouted.

While the people were shouting, Moses heard God's voice. "When will these people learn to trust Me? I have shown them My power, yet they are afraid. They must be punished!"

Moses stood before the people. "SILENCE!" he called. "You have not learned to trust the Lord. You are not the people who belong in the Land of Canaan. For forty years you must live in the wilderness. Your children will be braver than you. They will march into the Promised Land without you!"

The Hebrews' hearts were sad.

They lived in the wilderness for forty years until most of the old people died. Their children grew up strong and brave.

Moses knew he could never enter the Promised Land. He was old and tired. One day Moses climbed to the top of Mount Nebo. He took one last look at the land of Canaan and disappeared.

No one knows where Moses is buried, but his name will never be forgotten. He was the greatest leader the Hebrews ever had.